Kathryn & Elizabeth go Shopping

Written By Sarabeth O'Neil

Illustrated & Designed by Jennifer Zivoin

To my step-daughters, the real Kathryn and Elizabeth,
and my son Gordon. You have brought so much joy
into my life and inspire me more than you will ever know!
-S.O.

For Mom & Dad,
Rome & Olivia
-J.Z.

Two little girls, Kathryn and Elizabeth, received their
allowance on Saturday morning.

"Here is your allowance," their dad said handing
money to Kathryn, "and here is yours, Elizabeth."

Elizabeth immediately ran to put the money into her piggy bank, which was stuffed. Kathryn ran past her empty piggy bank on her dresser happily singing,

"Let's go shopping! shopping, shopping, shopping!"

"Katie!" Elizabeth called after her, "You know you don't **HAVE** to spend your money right away!" But Kathryn had already run to find her father. "Dad!" she exclaimed "We have to go shopping right away!"

As the girls were leaving the house with their father, Kathryn, who had stuffed her allowance into her coat pocket turned to her sister and said, "Aren't you bringing your money with you, Lizzy?"

Elizabeth explained, "I don't want to lose it and I don't want to spend any until I'm really sure of what I want."

When Kathryn and Elizabeth arrived at the toy store, Kathryn immediately ran to the first aisle, pointing at everything she saw. First, she spied a doll in a bright pink box wearing a purple party dress.

As she ran to excitedly grab it from the shelf, Elizabeth protested. "Katie, you already have, like, a billion dolls already!"

Kathryn thought about this for a moment and decided to move on. She then saw a display of watches with animal faces. "I have to have one!" she cried in excitement. She grabbed a kitty watch and declared, "It's purrrrfect!"

She giggled and started to walk off with it, but Elizabeth called after her, "But Katie, you bought a princess watch a month ago and never even wear it!"

Kathryn considered this for a moment, set down the watch and walked on. She knew her sister was right, but she really wanted to buy *something!*

As the sisters walked down the next aisle, Elizabeth noticed a cooking set on the shelf and wandered over to look at it. She loved cooking and this would be something she would really enjoy.

"You should definitely buy that, Lizzy! You love cooking." Kathryn said.

Elizabeth scrunched her face in thought, traced her finger around the box and then stepped back. "No," she finally said, "I like it a lot, but I'm just not sure that's what I want to spend my money on."

Kathryn shrugged, not understanding her sister at all.

Kathryn then looked in the opposite direction and spotted a stuffed giraffe taller than her and once again declared that she must have it.

"Even you must think this is cool, Lizzy! He's sooo big! He's the best thing ever!" Kathryn said as she wrapped her arms around the giraffe.

Elizabeth tried to reason with her sister, she already had lots of stuffed animals at home that she never even played with. "Katie, if you buy him, we will need a bigger bedroom! He'll take up half of it!" Elizabeth said, her eyes wide in awe at a toy that size.

Kathryn ignored her sister's advice, deciding to buy the giraffe after all. As she struggled to drag her new friend to the counter, she noticed a bin of sparkly bouncy balls next to the cash register. She reached into the bin to grab a bright yellow one as her sister caught up with her.

"Katie! Now you are buying something else? You should stop and think about that. You didn't even want one of those until you saw it! I bet you'll never even play with it!"

Kathryn crossed her arms, "It's only $1.00 Lizzy, and I want it!" She put the ball next to the giraffe's tag on the counter and handed money to the cashier. Elizabeth walked out of the store with their father and Kathryn with her new toys.

While they rode home in their car, Kathryn looked out her window and saw one of her favorite stores. She loved going there to buy jewelry.

"Oh, Daddy, I need to go to that store too! Please, it's very important!"

Elizabeth just sighed.

Kathryn and Elizabeth walked into the store and began looking at everything displayed on the brightly colored walls. There were racks covered with necklaces, sunglasses, purses and more.

Kathryn was ecstatic.

She rushed straight to the sales bin. There was a sign on top of the bin that read, "Any 10 items for only $5.00!!!" Kathryn squealed and began pulling items out of the bin, excited she could buy so many things for so little money.

"Oh Katie! Would you even want any of those things if they weren't on sale?" Elizabeth asked her sister earnestly.

"Are you kidding?" Kathryn asked excitedly, "These are all so fashionable! I love them!"

Elizabeth continued to protest, but Kathryn ignored her sister. She was getting tired of all Elizabeth's questions and comments. She knew what she wanted and that was that!

Kathryn walked past her sister up to the counter with her armful of headbands, bracelets and glittery necklaces.

As Kathryn put her items on the counter one by one, Elizabeth pointed out, "Katie, you know you already have a dolphin necklace just like this one."

Kathryn studied the necklace and said, "No, this one is different…I think…"

Kathryn, Elizabeth and their dad left the store. Kathryn put her second bag into the car. Elizabeth still did not have any bags.

When the girls arrived home, Kathryn started to look her new purchases over.

She dragged her new giraffe into the corner of her room. She looked at him for a minute and then placed a doll from her overstuffed toy box on top of his fuzzy head. She began to realize that maybe he was a bit **BIG**.

    Then Kathryn took the bouncy ball out of the bag. She bounced it a couple times on her bedroom floor before getting bored with it.

    "Well, that's not very fun." Kathryn said grumpily, and tossed the ball into the corner of her room. Kathryn then set the bag from the jewelry store on her dresser and looked around her room.

"Lizzy! I'm bored!"

She yelled out towards the living room.
"What should we do now?"

Elizabeth said she wanted to go to the
book store to look around.

Soon after, the sisters arrived at the book store. Kathryn looked around and quickly spotted a display for a movie that has just come out.

"Oh, wow!" she exclaimed, "This is sooo cool! I am definitely getting it! I've wanted to see this movie forever!"

Elizabeth, who had followed her sister, scrunched her face and asked, "Um, Katie….do you even have any money left?"

Kathryn reached into her pocket. She had only a few coins left.

Kathryn thought for a minute.
She really wanted to get the movie.
She knew there had to be a way.

"Hmmm…well, this is no problem." She finally declared, "I will just ask Mom to get us more money from the ATM machine to buy it!" She began walking towards her mother.

"Katie, that's not how it works!" Elizabeth protested. "Mom and Dad have to work for that money. They only get so much and it has to pay for everything: our house, our car, our food, everything! Once it's gone, it's gone. They can't just keep taking money out!"

"Well…" Kathryn said slowly, trying to come up with a new plan. "No problem, Lizzy! Mom has a credit card too! I'll ask her to use the credit card to buy my movie!"

"Oh Katie," Elizabeth shook her head, "that's even worse.

When you use a credit card, you're using someone else's money. You have to pay it back plus extra for using it in the first place. That's called interest."

Kathryn then had another thought. "I know, Lizzy!" she said "You could buy it for us! You have lots of money!"

Elizabeth shook her head responding, "I think I'll just wait until it's on TV. You should have saved your money if you really wanted it."

Kathryn put the movie back on the shelf and sulked as she and her sister walked out of the store with their mother.

Back at home, Kathryn and Elizabeth walked into their bedroom to play. "I just can't believe I'm all out of money!" exclaimed Kathryn. "I don't even have anything good to play with. I am so bored!"

Elizabeth looked around her sister's side of the room. There were toys everywhere. Many of them were still unopened.

"Katie, look around you! If you could trade all these things you don't even play with for the money you paid for them, you'd be rich!"

Kathryn shrugged sadly and laid down on her bed, surrounded by toys she didn't even want.

Elizabeth climbed up on her bed and leaned back. She began to daydream about all the things she could do with the money she had been saving. She wasn't sure what she would use it for yet, but she knew that when she did...